The Wheels of the Bus

Go Round and Round

MUSIC ARRANGED BY PATTY ZEITLIN

The
Wheels of the Bus
Go
Round and Round

School Bus Songs and Chants

Collected by NANCY LARRICK

Illustrated by Gene Holtan

Golden Gate Junior Books

San Carlos, California

To These My Special Thanks

For help in collecting these school bus songs and chants and
in tracking down elusive lines and melodies, I am deeply
indebted to a number of my former students in
the School of Education at Lehigh University—
Kay Winters,
Jeannette Stackhouse,
Kathy McCain,
Polly Long,
Linda Zimmerman,
Cynthia Gordon,
Kathleen Mattes,
Marlene Mantz,
and Joanne Perich—
all of them wonderfully creative teachers with a
keen ear for poetry in the oral literature of childhood.

Nancy Larrick

Text copyright © 1972 by Nancy Larrick Crosby
Illustrations copyright © 1972 by Gene Holtan
All rights reserved
ISBNs: Trade 0-87464-190-X   Library 0-87464-191-8
Library of Congress catalog card number 72-76936
Lithographed in the United States of America
by Anderson, Ritchie and Simon, Los Angeles

As the Wheels of the Bus Go Round and Round

IN THE UNITED STATES more than twenty million youngsters travel by school bus every school day of the year. Usually the school bus ride takes half an hour to an hour each way. In sparsely populated areas, travel time for each child is much longer. Always the route is the same, with the same stops morning and evening, the same passengers filing into their great pumpkin-yellow bus.

As "the wheels of the bus go round and round," young school commuters often break into song or chant familiar rhymes and jingles. Some of the songs are the ones that grandparents and great-grandparents were singing when they were children. Some are new verses to old tunes. Often the words are so timely that they might have been created that very day.

Every child seems to know them—not because he has seen them in print, but because he has heard them so many times that they are his. Indeed, he knows so many variations that he feels free to toss in his own new words or lines, even while the song is underway.

The songs and chants in this collection have been reported by hundreds of young school bus riders. These are part of the oral literature of childhood, seldom recorded, but ringing in the ears of children riding to and from school each day.

The Wheels of the Bus

6.

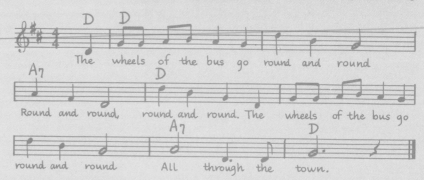

The wheels of the bus go round and round
Round and round, round and round.
The wheels of the bus go round and round
All through the town.

The driver on the bus says, "Step to the rear!
Step to the rear! Step to the rear!"
The driver on the bus says, "Step to the rear!"
All through the town.

Go Round and Round

The people on the bus go up and down
Up and down, up and down.
The people on the bus go up and down
All through the town.

The kids on the bus go *yakkity-yak*
Yakkity-yak, yakkity-yak.
The kids on the bus go *yakkity-yak*
All through the town.

The driver on the bus says, "Quiet, please!
Quiet, please! Quiet, please!"
The driver on the bus says, "Quiet, please!"
All through the town.

The wheels of the bus go round and round
Round and round, round and round.
The wheels of the bus go round and round
All through the town.

8. Who Stole the Cookies from the Cookie Jar?

Questions and answers are chanted by groups and individuals with a new name used in each stanza.

Who stole the cookies from the cookie jar?
   Jimmy stole the cookies from the cookie jar.
Who me?
   Yes, you.
Not me.
   Then who?

Who stole the cookies from the cookie jar?
   Peter stole the cookies from the cookie jar.
Who me?
   Yes, you.
Not me.
   Then who?

Who stole the cookies from the cookie jar?
   Debra stole the cookies from the cookie jar.
Who me?
   Yes, you.
Not me.
   Then who?

Johnny Over the Ocean

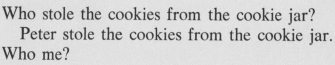

Johnny over the ocean
Johnny over the sea
Johnny broke a milk bottle
And blamed it on me.

I told Ma
And Ma told Pa
Johnny got a lickin'
And a Ha! Ha! Ha!

10. The Ants Go Marching One by One

The ants go marching one by one
   Hurrah! Hurrah!
The ants go marching one by one
   Hurrah! Hurrah!
When the ants go marching one by one
The little one stops to suck his thumb
And they all go marching down to the earth
   to get out of the rain—
     BOOM, BOOM, BOOM, BOOM, BOOM, BOOM, BOOM, BOOM!

The ants go marching two by two
   Hurrah! Hurrah!
The ants go marching two by two
   Hurrah! Hurrah!
When the ants go marching two by two
The little one stops to tie his shoe
And they all go marching down to the earth
   to get out of the rain—
     BOOM, BOOM, BOOM, BOOM, BOOM, BOOM, BOOM, BOOM!

The ants go marching three by three
    Hurrah! Hurrah!
The ants go marching three by three
    Hurrah! Hurrah!
When the ants go marching three by three
The little one stops to climb a tree
And they all go marching down to the earth
    to get out of the rain—
      BOOM, BOOM, BOOM, BOOM, BOOM, BOOM, BOOM, BOOM!

The ants go marching four by four
    Hurrah! Hurrah!
The ants go marching four by four
    Hurrah! Hurrah!
When the ants go marching four by four
The little one stops to shut the door
And they all go marching down to the earth
    to get out of the rain—
      BOOM, BOOM, BOOM, BOOM, BOOM, BOOM, BOOM, BOOM!

The ants go marching five by five
    Hurrah! Hurrah!
The ants go marching five by five
    Hurrah! Hurrah!
When the ants go marching five by five
The little one stops to kick a hive
And they all go marching down to the earth
    to get out of the rain—
      BOOM, BOOM, BOOM, BOOM, BOOM, BOOM, BOOM, BOOM!

The ants go marching six by six
    Hurrah! Hurrah!
The ants go marching six by six
    Hurrah! Hurrah!
When the ants go marching six by six
The little one stops to pick up sticks
And they all go marching down to the earth
    to get out of the rain—
      BOOM, BOOM, BOOM, BOOM, BOOM, BOOM, BOOM, BOOM!

The ants go marching seven by seven
  Hurrah! Hurrah!
The ants go marching seven by seven
  Hurrah! Hurrah!
When the ants go marching seven by seven
The little one stops to go to heaven
And they all go marching down to the earth
  to get out of the rain—
    Boom, boom, boom, boom, boom, boom, boom, boom!

The ants go marching eight by eight
  Hurrah! Hurrah!
The ants go marching eight by eight
  Hurrah! Hurrah!
When the ants go marching eight by eight
The little one stops to shut the gate
And they all go marching down to the earth
  to get out of the rain—
    Boom, boom, boom, boom, boom, boom, boom, boom!

The ants go marching nine by nine
  Hurrah! Hurrah!
The ants go marching nine by nine
  Hurrah! Hurrah!
When the ants go marching nine by nine
The little one stops to pick up a dime
And they all go marching down to the earth
  to get out of the rain—
    Boom, boom, boom, boom, boom, boom, boom, boom!

The ants go marching ten by ten
  Hurrah! Hurrah!
The ants go marching ten by ten
  Hurrah! Hurrah!
When the ants go marching ten by ten
The little one stops to shout THE END
And they all go marching down to the earth
  to get out of the rain—
    Boom, boom, boom, boom, boom, boom, boom, boom!

Ding Dong Bell

Ding dong bell
My cat fell in the well
It took six big men
To pull her out and then

Ding dong bell
She fell back in the well
We got her with a net
But she looked sad and wet.

Ding dong bell
We've got a cat to sell.

Ding dong bell My cat fell in the well

It took six big men To pull her out and then

14. The Bear Went Over the Mountain

The bear went over the mountain
The bear went over the mountain
The bear went over the mountain
And what do you think he saw?

The other side of the mountain
The other side of the mountain
The other side of the mountain
And what do you think he saw?

Grass on the side of the mountain
Grass on the side of the mountain
Grass on the side of the mountain
And what do you think he saw?

A tree in the grass on the mountain
A tree in the grass on the mountain
A tree in the grass on the mountain
And what do you think he saw?

A nest in the tree on the mountain
A nest in the tree on the mountain
A nest in the tree on the mountain
And what do you think he saw?

A bird in the nest on the mountain
A bird in the nest on the mountain
A bird in the nest on the mountain
And what do you think he saw?

A flea on the bird in the mountain
A flea on the bird in the mountain
A flea on the bird in the mountain
And what do you think he saw?

An eye on the flea in the mountain
An eye on the flea in the mountain
An eye on the flea in the mountain
And that is what he saw.

B-I-N-G-O

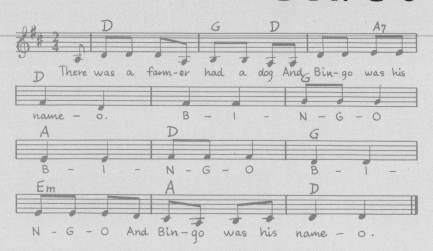

There was a farmer had a dog
And Bingo was his name-o.
B-I-N-G-O
B-I-N-G-O
B-I-N-G-O
And Bingo was his name-o.

There was a farmer had a dog
And Bingo was his name-o.
B-I-N-G-__
B-I-N-G-__
B-I-N-G-__
And Bingo was his name-o.

There was a farmer had a dog
And Bingo was his name-o.
B-I-N-__-__
B-I-N-__-__
B-I-N-__-__
And Bingo was his name-o.

There was a farmer had a dog
And Bingo was his name-o.
B-I-__-__-__
B-I-__-__-__
B-I-__-__-__
And Bingo was his name-o.

There was a farmer had a dog
And Bingo was his name-o.
B-__-__-__-__
B-__-__-__-__
B-__-__-__-__
And Bingo was his name-o.

There was a farmer had a dog
And Bingo was his name-o.
__-__-__-__-__
__-__-__-__-__
__-__-__-__-__
And Bingo was his name.

18.

Here We Go Looby-loo

Here we go Loo-by-loo Here we go Loo-by-light Here we go Loo-by-loo All on a Sat-ur-day night. I put my right hand in I take my right hand out I give my right hand a shake, shake, shake and turn my-self a-bout.

Here we go Looby-loo
Here we go Looby-light
Here we go Looby-loo
All on a Saturday night.

I put my right hand in
I take my right hand out
I give my right hand a shake, shake, shake
And turn myself about.

Here we go Looby-loo
Here we go Looby-light
Here we go Looby-loo
All on a Saturday night.

I put my left hand in
I take my left hand out
I give my left hand a shake, shake, shake
And turn myself about.

Here we go Looby-loo
Here we go Looby-light
Here we go Looby-loo
All on a Saturday night.

I put my right foot in
I take my right foot out
I give my right foot a shake, shake, shake
And turn myself about.

Here we go Looby-loo
Here we go Looby-light
Here we go Looby-loo
All on a Saturday night.

I put my left foot in
I take my left foot out
I give my left foot a shake, shake, shake
And turn myself about.

Here we go Looby-loo
Here we go Looby-light
Here we go Looby-loo
All on a Saturday night.

I put my whole self in
I take my whole self out
I give my self a shake, shake, shake
And turn myself about.

Here we go Looby-loo
Here we go Looby-light
Here we go Looby-loo
All on a Saturday night.

20. If You're Happy and You Know It

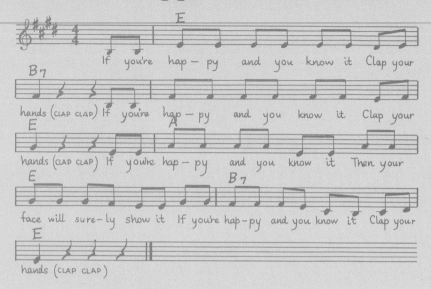

If you're happy and you know it
Clap your hands [CLAP CLAP]
If you're happy and you know it
Clap your hands [CLAP CLAP]
If you're happy and you know it
Then your face will surely show it
If you're happy and you know it
Clap your hands [CLAP CLAP]

If you're angry and you know it
Stamp your feet [STAMP STAMP]
If you're angry and you know it
Stamp your feet [STAMP STAMP]
If you're angry and you know it
Your face will surely show it
If you're angry and you know it
Stamp your feet [STAMP STAMP]

If you're sad and you know it
Shed a tear [SNIFF SNIFF]
If you're sad and you know it
Shed a tear [SNIFF SNIFF]
If you're sad and you know it
Your face will surely show it
If you're sad and you know it
Shed a tear [SNIFF SNIFF]

If you're weary and you know it
Heave a sigh [WHEE-YOU]
If you're weary and you know it
Heave a sigh [WHEE-YOU]
If you're weary and you know it
Your face will surely show it
If you're weary and you know it
Heave a sigh [WHEE-YOU]

If you're joyous and you know it
Click your heels [CLICK CLICK]
If you're joyous and you know it
Click your heels [CLICK CLICK]
If you're joyous and you know it
Your face will surely show it
If you're joyous and you know it
Click your heels [CLICK CLICK]

22. Do You Hate Your Teachers Dear?

TUNE:
MARY HAD
A LITTLE LAMB

Do you hate your teachers dear,
Teachers dear, teachers dear?
Do you hate your teachers dear?
Then throw them out the window.

Yes, we hate our teachers dear,
Teachers dear, teachers dear.
Yes, we hate our teachers dear.
We'll throw them out the window.

Ta-Ra-Ra Boom-De-Ay

Ta-ra-ra boom-de-ay
We had no school today
The teacher passed away
Ta-ra-ra boom-de-ay.

Ta-ra-ra boom-de-ay
We threw her in the bay
The sharks had lunch today
Ta-ra-ra boom-de-ay.

Found A Peanut

24.

Found a pea-nut, found a pea-nut Found a
pea-nut just- now Just now I found a
pea-nut Found a pea-nut just now.

TUNE: Clementine

Found a peanut, found a peanut
Found a peanut just now
Just now I found a peanut
Found a peanut just now.

Cracked it open, cracked it open
Cracked it open just now
Just now I cracked it open
Cracked it open just now.

It was rotten, it was rotten
It was rotten just now
Just now it was rotten
It was rotten just now.

Ate it anyway, ate it anyway
Ate it anyway just now
Just now I ate it anyway
Ate it anyway just now.

Got a stomach ache, got a stomach ache
Got a stomach ache just now
Just now I got a stomach ache
Got a stomach ache just now.

Called a doctor, called a doctor
Called a doctor just now
Just now I called a doctor
Called a doctor just now.

Died anyway, died anyway
Died anyway just now
Just now I died anyway
Died anyway just now.

Went to heaven, went to heaven
Went to heaven just now
Just now I went to heaven
Went to heaven just now.

Met St. Peter, met St. Peter
Met St. Peter just now
Just now I met St. Peter
Met St. Peter just now.

Ate a peanut, ate a peanut
Ate a peanut just now
Just now I ate a peanut
Ate a peanut just now.

Inky Dinky Spider

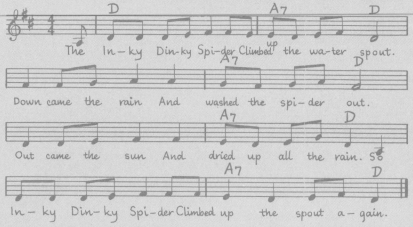

The In—ky Din—ky Spi—der Climbed up the wa—ter spout.

Down came the rain And washed the spi—der out.

Out came the sun And dried up all the rain. So

In—ky Din—ky Spi—der Climbed up the spout a—gain.

Inky Dinky Spider
Climbed up the waterspout.
Down came the rain
And washed the spider out.
Out came the sun
And dried up all the rain.
So the Inky Dinky Spider
Climbed up the spout again.

I Had a Little Brother

I had a little brother
His name was Tiny Tim.
I put him in the bathtub
To teach him how to swim.

He drank up all the water
He ate up all the soap.
He died last night
With a bubble in his throat.

In came the doctor,
In came the nurse,
In came a lady
With a big fat purse.

Dead said the doctor.
Dead said the nurse.
Dead said the lady
With the big fat purse.

So out went the doctor
Out went the nurse
And out went the lady
With the big fat purse.

On Top of Spaghetti

On top of spa-ghet-ti All cov-ered with cheese I lost my poor meat-ball When some-bo-dy sneezed.

TUNE:
ON TOP OF OLD SMOKEY

On top of spaghetti
All covered with cheese
I lost my poor meatball
When somebody sneezed.

It rolled off the table
And onto the floor
And then my poor meatball
Rolled out of the door.

It rolled in the garden
And under a bush
And then my poor meatball
Was nothing but mush.

Then early next summer
It grew into a tree.
It grew lovely meatballs
All ready for me.

If you eat spaghetti
All covered with cheese
Hold onto your meatball
And don't ever sneeze.

Ninety-Nine Bottles of Beer

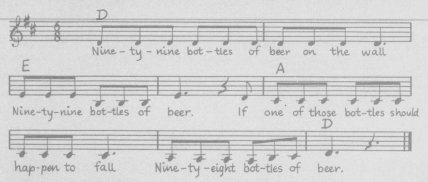

Nine-ty-nine bot-tles of beer on the wall
Nine-ty-nine bot-tles of beer. If one of those bot-tles should
hap-pen to fall Nine-ty-eight bot-tles of beer.

Ninety-nine bottles of beer on the wall
Ninety-nine bottles of beer.
If one of those bottles should happen to fall
Ninety-eight bottles of beer.

Ninety-eight bottles of beer on the wall
Ninety-eight bottles of beer.
If one of those bottles should happen to fall
Ninety-seven bottles of beer.

Ninety-seven bottles of beer on the wall
Ninety-seven bottles of beer.
If one of those bottles should happen to fall
Ninety-six bottles of beer.

Ninety-six bottles of beer on the wall
Ninety-six bottles of beer.
If one of those bottles should happen to fall
Ninety-five bottles of beer.

Ninety-five bottles of beer on the wall
Ninety-five bottles of beer.
If one of those bottles should happen to fall
Ninety-four bottles of beer.

*Continue
the count-down
until the bottles
—or your energy—
give out.*

Ninety-four bottles of beer on the wall
Ninety-four bottles of beer.
If one of those bottles should happen to fall
Ninety-three bottles of beer.

Ten in the Bed

There were ten in the bed and the little one said,
"Roll over. Roll over."
So they all rolled over and one fell out —

There were nine in the bed and the little one said,
"Roll over. Roll over."
So they all rolled over and one fell out —

There were eight in the bed and the little one said,
"Roll over. Roll over."
So they all rolled over and one fell out —

There were seven in the bed and the little one said,
"Roll over. Roll over."
So they all rolled over and one fell out —

There were six in the bed and the little one said,
"Roll over. Roll over."
So they all rolled over and one fell out —

There were five in the bed and the little one said,
"Roll over. Roll over."
So they all rolled over and one fell out —

There were four in the bed and the little one said,
"Roll over. Roll over."
So they all rolled over and one fell out —

There were three in the bed and the little one said,
"Roll over. Roll over."

So they all rolled over and one fell out —

There were two in the bed and the little one said,
"Roll over. Roll over."
So they all rolled over and one fell out —

There was one in the bed and the little one said,
"GOOD NIGHT!"

Teddy Bear, Teddy Bear

Teddy Bear, Teddy Bear, turn around
Teddy Bear, Teddy Bear, touch the ground.
Teddy Bear, Teddy Bear, shine your shoe
Teddy Bear, Teddy Bear, I love you.
Teddy Bear, Teddy Bear, go upstairs
Teddy Bear, Teddy Bear, say your prayers.
Teddy Bear, Teddy Bear, switch off the light
Teddy Bear, Teddy Bear, say Goodnight.

Mary and Peter Sittin' in a Tree

Mary and Peter sittin' in a tree
K-I-S-S-I-N-G
First comes love, then comes marriage
Then comes Mary with a baby carriage.

Cinderella Dressed in Yellow

Cinderella dressed in yellow
Went upstairs to kiss her fellow
Made a mistake and kissed a snake
How many doctors did it take?
1 - 2 - 3 - 4 - 5 - 6 - 7 - - - - - -

36. Shoot A Cat

Shoot a cat.
Shoot a rat.
Shoot the dirty
Democrat.

Shoot a turkey.
Shoot a hen.
Shoot the dirty
Republican.

I Saw You in the Ocean

I saw you in the ocean
I saw you in the sea
I saw you in the bathtub
Oops! Pardon me.

First Grade Babies

First grade babies
Second grade brats
Third grade angels
Fourth grade rats
Fifth grade teachers
Sixth grade plums
All the rest
Are dirty bums.

Roses are Wilted

Roses are wilted
Violets are dead
The sugar bowl is empty
And so is your head.

Roses are Red

Roses are red
Violets are blue
The skunks had a college
And named it P.U.

The Foolish Frog

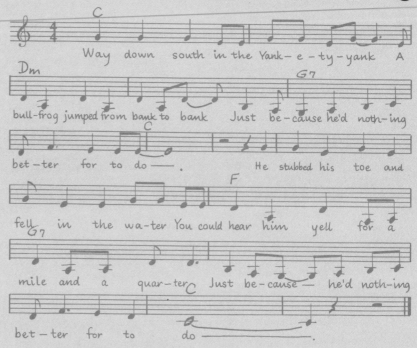

Way down south in the Yank—e—ty—yank A
bull-frog jumped from bank to bank Just be—cause he'd noth—ing
bet—ter for to do——. He stubbed his toe and
fell in the wa—ter You could hear him yell for a
mile and a quar—ter Just be—cause—— he'd noth—ing
bet—ter for to do——.

Way down south in the Yankety-yank
A bullfrog jumped from bank to bank
Just because he'd nothing better for to do.

He stubbed his toe and fell in the water
You could hear him yell for a mile and a quarter
Just because he'd nothing better for to do.

Merry-Go-Round

The more we get together
Together, together,
The more we get together
The happier we'll be.

For your friends are my friends
And my friends are your friends,
The more we get together
The happier we'll be.

To imitate the music of
the merry-go-round as
background for the song,
divide into four groups.

1. One will sing the words.

2. One will repeat the
sound OOM-PA-PA,
OOM-PA-PA on a low note
throughout.

3. One will repeat the
sound OOM-SISS-SISS,
OOM-SISS-SISS on a slightly
higher note throughout.

4. The fourth will
repeat the sound OOM-
TWEEDLE-DEE, OOM-
TWEEDLE-DEE on a very
high note throughout.

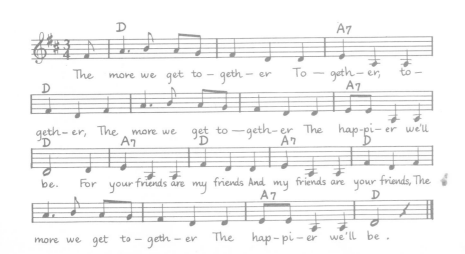

40. It Takes a Worried Man

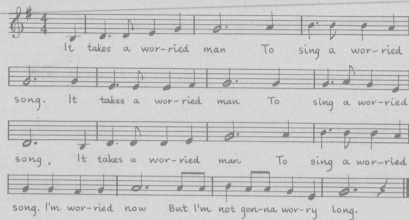

It takes a wor-ried man To sing a wor-ried
song. It takes a wor-ried man To sing a wor-ried
song. It takes a wor-ried man To sing a wor-ried
song. I'm wor-ried now   But I'm not gon-na wor-ry long.

It takes a worried man
To sing a worried song.
It takes a worried man
To sing a worried song.
It takes a worried man
To sing a worried song.
I'm worried now
But I'm not gonna worry long.

It takes a happy man
To sing a happy song.
It takes a happy man
To sing a happy song.
It takes a happy man
To sing a happy song.
I'm happy now
And I'll be happy all along.

It takes a loving man
To sing a loving song.
It takes a loving man
To sing a loving song.
It takes a loving man
To sing a loving song
I'm loving now
And I'll be loving all along.

The Little Bullfrog

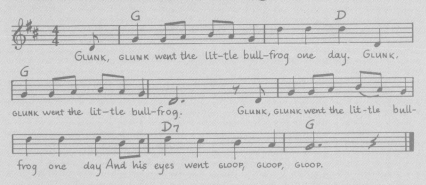

GLUNK, GLUNK went the little bullfrog one day.
GLUNK, GLUNK went the little bullfrog.
GLUNK, GLUNK went the little bullfrog one day
And his eyes went GLOOP, GLOOP, GLOOP.

This Old Man

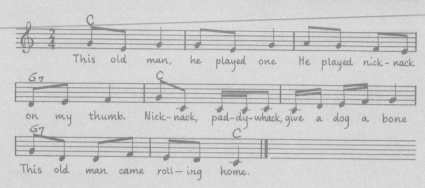

This old man, he played one
He played nick-nack on my thumb.
Nick-nack, paddy-whack, give a dog a bone
This old man came rolling home.

This old man, he played two
He played nick-nack on my shoe.
Nick-nack, paddy-whack, give a dog a bone
This old man came rolling home.

This old man, he played three
He played nick-nack on my knee.
Nick-nack, paddy-whack, give a dog a bone
This old man came rolling home.

This old man, he played four
He played nick-nack on my door.
Nick-nack, paddy-whack, give a dog a bone
This old man came rolling home.

This old man, he played five
He played nick-nack on my hive.
Nick-nack, paddy-whack, give a dog a bone
This old man came rolling home.

This old man, he played six
He played nick-nack on my sticks.
Nick-nack, paddy-whack, give a dog a bone
This old man came rolling home.

This old man, he played seven
He played nick-nack 'til eleven.
Nick-nack, paddy-whack, give a dog a bone
This old man came rolling home.

This old man, he played eight
He played nick-nack on my pate.
Nick-nack, paddy-whack, give a dog a bone
This old man came rolling home.

This old man, he played nine
He played nick-nack on my spine.
Nick-nack, paddy-whack, give a dog a bone
This old man came rolling home.

This old man, he played ten
He played nick-nack now and then.
Nick-nack, paddy-whack, give a dog a bone
This old man came rolling home.

44.

The Billboard

As I was walk-ing down the street One dark and dreary day I came up-on a bill-board And much to my dis-may The sign was torn and tat-tered From the rain the night be-fore But clear-ly I could fig-ure out The mess-age that it bore—: T-I-D-E Cheer!

As I was walking down the street
One dark and dreary day
I came upon a billboard
And much to my dismay
The sign was torn and tattered
From the rain the night before
But clearly I could figure out
The message that it bore:

Smoke Coca-Cola cigarettes
Chew Wrigley Spearmint beer
Ken-L Ration dog food
Makes your wife's complexion clear
Simonize your baby
With a Hershey candy bar
Texaco's the beauty cream
That's used by every star.

So take your next vacation
In a brand new Frigidaire
Learn to play the piano
In your winter underwear
Doctors say that babies
Should smoke when they are three.
And people over 65
Should bathe in Lipton tea.

T-I-D-E Cheer!

46.

Oh, You Can't Get to Heaven

Oh, you can't get to heaven in a rocking chair
'Cause a rocking chair won't get you there
Oh, you can't get to heaven in a rocking chair
'Cause a rocking chair won't get you there
But I ain't gonna grieve, my Lord, no more
I ain't gonna grieve, my Lord, no more.

Oh, you can't get to heaven on roller skates
'Cause you'll roll right by St. Peter's gates
You can't get to heaven on roller skates
'Cause you'll roll right by St. Peter's gates
But I ain't gonna grieve, my Lord, no more
I ain't gonna grieve, my Lord, no more.

Oh, you can't get to heaven in _____'s car
'Cause _____'s car won't go that far
You can't get to heaven in _____'s car
'Cause _____'s car won't go that far
But I ain't gonna grieve, my Lord, no more
I ain't gonna grieve, my Lord, no more.

Oh, you can't get to heaven on a rocket ship
'Cause a rocket ship won't make the trip
You can't get to heaven on a rocket ship
'Cause a rocket ship won't make the trip
But I ain't gonna grieve, my Lord, no more
I ain't gonna grieve, my Lord, no more.

Oh, you can't get to heaven with Superman
'Cause our good Lord is a Batman fan
You can't get to heaven with Superman
'Cause our good Lord is a Batman fan
But I ain't gonna grieve, my Lord, no more
I ain't gonna grieve, my Lord, no more.

Index of First Lines